A line of people waited to see

the haunted 🏚.

🧑 and 🐕 took their 🎫 and

put them in a 📦.

One little girl, Amy, was scared.

She didn't like the 👻 or the 🎃.

🧑 said, "It is just make-believe."

"I am not a real 👻," said 👧.

But 🐕 doesn't like the 🎃

either, Amy thought.

THE HAUNTED PUMPKINS

By Michelle H. Nagler
Illustrated by Duendes del Sur

First published in this format in 2014 by Curious Fox,
an imprint of Capstone Global Library Limited,
7 Pilgrim Street, London, EC4V 6LB
– Registered company number: 6695582
www.curious-fox.com

CAPG33853

Originated by Capstone Global Library Ltd
Printed and Bound in Slovakia by TBB

ISBN 978 1 782 02211 4
18 17 16 15 14
10 9 8 7 6 5 4 3 2 1

A CIP catalogue record for this book is available
from the British Library.

The National Literacy Trust is a registered charity no: 1116260 and a company limited by
guarantee no. 5836486 registered in England and Wales and a registered charity in Scotland
no. SC042944. Registered address: 68 South Lambeth Road, London SW8 1RL.
National Literacy Trust logo and reading tips © National Literacy Trust 2014
www.literacytrust.org.uk/donate

™

 and his friends were making

a haunted 🏚 for Halloween.

They hung 🕸 on the 🪟.

They carved scary faces on 🎃.

 was scared of the 🎃.

👩 played a 💿 of scary sounds.

The 💿 said "Woo-oooh!" and

"Creeeeeak!" and "Boo!"

The next day, the  looked different. The was lying on the . were on the . "Like, maybe the really is haunted," said .

"Look!" said . "The are different!"

The were not scary anymore. thought they looked much better.

"Jinkies!" said . "Haunted

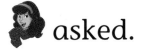 !"

"Let's look for clues," said .

 and I will look outside.

"Ro way!" said 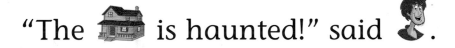.

"The is haunted!" said .

"Would you do it for two ?"

asked.

"Rokay!" said .

 and  heard a noise.

But it was just a  scratching the .

"Look!" yelled , "A !"

But it was only a creepy shadow on the .

 said, "Like, let's search the kitchen, ."

 used his  to find the way down the  to the kitchen.

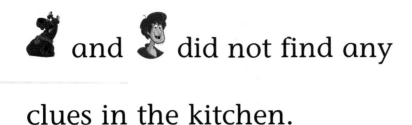 and 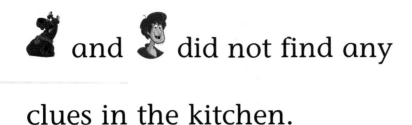 did not find any

clues in the kitchen.

But they did find a   on

the .

As they were eating the ,

they heard scary noises.

"Zoinks!" said. "It's the !"

 ran back up the and

out the .

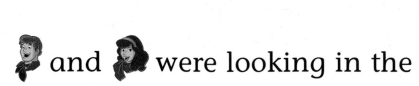 and were looking in the

 for clues.

"We heard the !" yelled .

"Reah!" said , running out the

.

slipped on some on the

and fell down the .

"Are you OK, ?" asked.

"Look!"  said, " found !"

 had landed on a pile of

near some .

"And a trail of too!" said .

"Let's follow them," said .

"Yeah," said. "Let's get away

from the in the !"

"That was no , ," said. "I

was just testing the of scary

noises."

The gang followed the and
.

The trail went around the 🏠.

It went around a 🌳.

The and stopped at a

bunch of smelly 🗑🗑.

"Yuck!" said 🧑.

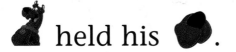 held his 🎩.

 looked inside the 🗑🗑 — and

found the scary 🎃🎃!

"What are the 🎃🎃 doing here?"

asked 👤.

"I have an idea," said 👩. "🐕,

can you keep following the

trail?"

🐕 put his 👃 to the ground.

The trail led to Amy's 🏠.

"See, it's not a 👻!" said 👩.

Amy said, " looked scared of the , so I switched them."

"And you knocked over the of by accident!" said .

"Oops!" said Amy. "I just wanted you to have happy ."

laughed. "Like, that makes me happy! We thought the was haunted."

barked. "Scooby-Dooby Doo!"

PICTURE CLUES

Did you have fun reading the picture clues in this Scooby-Doo mystery?

Reading is fun with Scooby-Doo!

house	Scooby	windows	webs
CD	pumpkin	ghost	Daphne
Fred	Velma	Shaggy	tickets
door	box	Scooby Snacks	table
tree	floor	stairs	pie
leaves	footprints	dustbins	nose